The author, Philip Jones, lives in Shrewsbury, where he sets his debut play, *The Lion Hotel*. After working in insurance, accountancy, and hospital administration until middle-age, he took the decision to return to full-time education in order to pursue his creative passions, gaining a first-class honours degree in English at University Centre Shrewsbury. An interest in local history was rekindled when he spent his work-based learning placement at *Shropshire Archives*, discovering the Victorian entertainments bill that forms part of the play's dialogue. He has since gone on to study for an MRes in Storytelling at the University of Chester.

Philip Jones

To my family, past and present.

Philip Jones

THE LION HOTEL

AUSTIN MACAULEY PUBLISHERS™

LONDON • CAMBRIDGE • NEW YORK • SHARJAH

A CIP catalogue record for this title is available from the British Library.

ISBN 9781788231367 (Paperback)
ISBN 9781788231381 (Hardback)
ISBN 9781788231374 (ePub e-book)
ISBN 9781398418165 (Audiobook)

www.austinmacauley.com

First Published (2021)
Austin Macauley Publishers Ltd
25, Canada Square
Canary Wharf
London
E14 5LQ

To my family for their support and enabling me to pursue my passion for creative writing. And to the staff and students at the University Centre Shrewsbury for their inspiration and expertise, in particular, the Class of 2019 and the English Department.

Table of Contents

Abstract

The Lion Hotel is a self-contained play that combines history and humour as it tells the story of how a detective's daughter ends up the suspect of a necklace theft. The play employs a variety of comic devices and mistaken motivations before the perpetrator is finally uncovered. The last two acts reflect on what has happened, as it becomes even clearer that there is a young detective in the making. There are many details from the history of Shrewsbury.

Play: The Lion Hotel (Character List)

Florence:	Inspector Horace's free-spirited daughter
Inspector Horace:	The best detective in his division
Violet Horace:	Inspector Horace's other third (his wife)
Receptionist:	The eyes and ears of the hotel
Waiter:	A man who doesn't know his left from his right
Waitress:	Practically dressed and another pair of hands
Lady:	The victim of a theft
Manager:	A man obsessed with protecting the reputation of his hotel
Amelia:	Florence's best friend at school, and probably outside of it, too
Mark:	The boy who steals Florence's shoe, and who Florence quite fancies, really
Kevin:	Florence's classroom heckler
Colin:	The boy from Florence's class who only speaks once, and that is just to inform everyone that he doesn't like organ music
Mr Collins:	Florence's head teacher and nemesis
Mr Old:	Florence's History teacher, who she finds it fun to make cheeky remarks to

Miss Charles:	Florence's English teacher, whose dark glasses make her something of a mystery, and who is forced to leave the class alone because of her memory
Porter:	A stand-in receptionist who seems to know rather too well how crime works
Towel Lady:	The lady who creates rather a soap opera
Amy:	Inspector Horace's favourite police receptionist

Act One
Scene One

Inspector 'Horace' and his daughter, 'Florence', arrive at 'The Lion Hotel' in Shrewsbury.
Inspector Horace is wearing his trademark red scarf, and Florence, the epitome of beauty, a pink dress which tones perfectly with her footwear choice.

Florence: "Father, I think we're stuck. We're not supposed to be in the same section of the revolving door."

Inspector Horace: "Hold on to my scarf, Florence, and I'll give the door an extra shove."

Florence: "This is so embarrassing."

Inspector Horace: "Where are your shoes, Florence?"

Florence: "Father, you're so Victorian. I thought we agreed that I only had to wear shoes for formal occasions."

Inspector Horace: "Don't you consider your mother's birthday a formal occasion?"

Florence: "No, not really. It normally takes place at home and without a father present."

Inspector Horace: "Unfortunately, detection is not a prediction."

Florence: "Surely you can control that, Father."

Inspector Horace: "It's going to be okay, Florence, we've made it to the other side, I can see reception."

Florence: "I'm so relieved, Father. Passing the lion above the door was scary enough. Making it through the door really shouldn't have been that difficult. Probably for you, Father, the scariest thing was seeing that temporary blackboard outside, with the menu on, which surely must have reminded you of school."

Inspector Horace: "I'm not sure that my old headmaster was ever as scary as yours is, Florence."

Florence: "Let's not talk about 'Mr Collins', Father. He only makes an example of me because I'm your daughter. Moreover, how was I supposed to know that he was measuring in inches when I was displaying in centimetres?"

Inspector Horace [*to the receptionist*]: "Good evening, young lady. My daughter and I are booked in for a meal in your Hayward Restaurant. My wife will be joining us shortly, in her own good time. Can you believe that her boss has her working on her birthday, and actually sells greetings cards?"

Receptionist: "I can believe it, sir. My boss had me working on my twenty-first birthday. I worked on reception in the morning, half-changed into a dress in one of the rooms in the afternoon, and then partied the night away upstairs in the evening. Now, if you and your daughter would like to make your way to the Tapestry Lounge, perhaps by the fireplace, one of the restaurant staff will call for you when they are ready; by that time, your wife may have arrived. Drinks are available if required."

Florence [*to the receptionist with her father potentially still within earshot*]: "The truth is that Mother and Father are like two figures inside a weather-house, they are rarely seen together."

[*The receptionist just smiles to acknowledge.*]

Receptionist: "I admire the bravery of your footwear choice, Miss. You remind me of my free-spirited sister, who once kicked off a party that way. What size and colour of shoes do you normally wear?"

Florence: "Size six and pink, but I don't want any from lost property. That happened in PE when I accidentally-on-purpose forgot my trainers, and I informed the teacher that I would rather brave the stinging nettles along the edge of the school field than accept any trainers a boy had worn."

Receptionist: "I wasn't going to offer you any, Miss. We don't have any lost property. A few lost guests, perhaps. My boyfriend can't help, either. The shoe shop where he works closes early on a Thursday."

Florence [*in soliloquy whilst following her father to the settee*]: "These were odd questions for the receptionist to have been asking. Why would she ask my shoe size and colour when there isn't any lost property? And surely a hotel this size should have some?"

Blackout

Act One
Scene Two

Florence has now caught up with her father and is sitting next to him.

Florence: "This is a very nice seating area, Father. The ancient stone fireplace and the carpet both remind me of home."

Inspector Horace: "Indeed, but why have you left your shoes in the car, Florence? I suppose the reason why you were wearing your new pink shoes every day last week, was to fool your father into thinking that you were doing the same this evening."

Florence: "Father, can't we talk about something else? Like the history of *The Lion Hotel* in Shrewsbury, perhaps? It's actually an old coaching inn, with a timber-framed middle section that dates back to the fifteenth century. And, to immediately move on four centuries, their famous nineteenth-century stagecoach, the *Wonder*, would travel between London and Shrewsbury in just sixteen hours. This might seem slow in today's terms, at an average speed of nearly ten miles per hour, but then it was really quick. Unlike today's buses, it was always on time, and so much so, the church clocks were reputed to have been regulated by it. And, did you know that John Nelson's lion, dating back to 1777, that lies proudly above the door, distracting you from entering the right section of the revolving door, took twenty-three books of gold leaf, containing twenty-five pages in each, at a cost of twenty pounds per book, to re-gild? And if I have my maths correct, that's eleven-thousand five-hundred pounds. It's a palace, Father, and Mother will think the same when she arrives."

Inspector Horace: "Florence, I found your monologue fascinating. Where did you learn all this from?"

Florence: "The Internet, Father. Where does anybody learn anything from these days?"

Inspector Horace: "And where can I learn it from?"

Florence: "Books, Father."

Inspector Horace: "Well, I never imagined it would be my daughter giving me the history lesson. And, the younger one is, the more history one has to begin to remember. I wonder where the waiter has got to. I was hoping not to have to order a drink until we made it into the restaurant."

Florence: "Unfortunately, Father, I'm the only free spirit here this evening."

Inspector Horace: "Florence, money doesn't grow on trees, you know."

Florence: "Actually it does, Father. I found a five-pound note in a tree at school. I handed it in, of course!"

Inspector Horace: "That's my daughter. As honest as a company who says that honesty is its policy."

Florence: "They are the worst kinds of companies, Father. If they say that they are honest, they usually aren't. And I thought that the waiter was supposed to wait on us, not the other way round. As for Mother, I hope that she has the right *Lion Hotel*. If she ends up at the one in your postcard collection, it doesn't bear thinking about."

Inspector Horace: "I presume, Florence, you are referring to the one in Dolgelley?"

Florence: "Yes, Father, because Wordsworth wrote in his Eighteenth-Century Chronicles: 'If you ever go to Dolgelley / Don't stay at the 'Lion Hotel', / There's nothing to put in your belly / And no one to answer the bell.' And you haven't helped with Mother's confusion, by covering up the dent on her car with a Welsh dragon sticker. Now, Mother can only sell her car in Wales or Hell."

Inspector Horace: "The dragon's lair is not the only one who can disguise and mislead."

Florence: "I can't think what you possibly mean, Father. Oh look, here comes the waiter. Or is that a penguin?"

Waiter: "We are almost nearly ready for you, sir. Can I offer you or your daughter a drink?"

Florence: "Wine, please."

Inspector Horace: "Florence, you know you're not old enough. Ignore my daughter, I often have to."

Florence: "Sometimes, being a child is like a tennis match. You get served, and then you end up with juice (deuce). If Father insists, I'll have a coke; but no ice to dilute it, or lemon to flavour it beyond recognition."

Inspector Horace: "Actually, I think we'll both wait until we are at our table, but keep the coke in mind for my daughter, who has been enlightening me about the history of this magnificent hotel, among other things."

Waiter: "The hotel does have a wonderful vintage, doesn't it? For example, the Dickens Suite upstairs is named after the famous novelist, Charles Dickens, who stayed in that very room."

Florence: "He stayed at the hotel in 1838 and 1858. A book of his letters, edited by his sister-in-law and his eldest daughter, confirms the fact."

Waiter: "Young lady, your knowledge of 'Charles Dickens' is as impressive as it is remarkable. I shall return in a few minutes to fetch you both to your table, after sorting out your cutlery. It is three sets that you need me to lay?"

Inspector Horace: "I do apologise for my wife's lateness. I can't think what is delaying her to this extent."

Florence [*after the waiter has disappeared*]: "Father, you don't think that Mother is having an affair? She has been on rather a lot of stocktakes recently."

Inspector Horace: "I think that I would know if your mother was having an affair. I am a detective, after all."

Florence: "Not necessarily, Father. Sophie's father didn't know, and he's one of your colleagues. She cried for a week when her father walked out, and now only has Internet contact with him."

Inspector Horace: "Would you cry if I left, Florence?"

Florence: "Yes, of course, Father. I would cry until my eyes were dry, and then find some onions to cry some more."

Inspector Horace: "This is presumably the Sophie who has a multitude of straps to have to undo to protect my living room carpet, every time she visits?"

Florence: "The very same. Except that Sophie only really has one strap to have to undo. The rest is just an act for your benefit, Father. It always makes me laugh the way she pretends like that. She is very fond of you, you know, Father."

Inspector Horace: "Well, I think you must invite Sophie over again, soon. And with regard to your mother, she might have her faults, like shopping in circles and incinerating food beyond recognition, but I trust her implicitly. I do wonder, however, how long a stocktake should take, and how often it should be necessary."

Florence: "Father, what was that bulge in the waiter's pocket? You must have noticed it, being a detective."

Inspector Horace: "Perhaps they are his instructions on how to lay the cutlery out."

Florence: "You might be right, Father, there is a correct way of doing it. I asked Mother once, but she didn't know, so I studied the dining table whilst watching an episode of *Downton Abbey*, and I was able to inform Mother afterwards that the correct order to eat is from the outside in. Surely it isn't that difficult to remember."

Inspector Horace: "It does seem logical. And how was school today, Florence?"

Florence: "Still there. The boys tried to burn down the science lab but got the formula wrong. And worse still, Melissa accidentally-on-purpose forgot her shoes and has stolen the part of Cinderella in the school play from me. But it won't be for long, I'm currently practising to win it back; I just can't remember which shoe Cinderella lost."

Inspector Horace: "Rather surprisingly, you seem to have both options covered, or rather uncovered, this evening. And how were your other subjects today, Florence?"

Florence: "Well, in English, the boys were so bad at answering the questions, any sensible answers were considered. And, in Geography, half the boys didn't even find their way to class."

Florence: "Look, Father, the waiter with the bulge is coming back. He reminds me of Lieutenant Columbo, the way he keeps returning."

Inspector Horace: "Perhaps, we are both Columbo's suspects?"

Florence: "I suppose we both look suspicious. I've already chosen the vegan option by dispensing with my leather shoes; and you, Father, are still wearing the red scarf that you always wear, despite it being such a warm evening."

Waiter: "I see that you have marginalised yourselves into the middle?"

Inspector Horace: "It was a bit warm by the fireplace."

Florence [*in soliloquy*]: "How can you marginalise yourself into the middle?"

Waiter: "If you follow me, sir, I will show you both to your table, where you will find the historic view through the window, as your daughter requested."

End of Act One

Act Two
Scene One

Florence is now seated in the restaurant at the same table as her father.

Florence: "I love my choice, Father. As I look through the window, and thankfully still before twilight, I can see 'the crookedest black and yellow old houses, all manner of shapes except straight shapes.'"

Inspector Horace: "A quotation from Charles Dickens' letters, I believe. But are you sure that you see yellow houses, Florence?"

Florence: "Okay, Father, we both know that they are white, but to say that would be to misquote Dickens."

Inspector Horace: "For the purposes of the tape, Florence, are those houses white or yellow?"

Florence: "You're not on duty now, Father. And neither is the waiter. He's disappeared again without taking our drinks order. My throat feels like a boy has his tongue half-way down it. But don't worry, Father, that's only a simile."

Inspector Horace: "That waitress over there doesn't appear to have any shoes on, either."

Florence: "Father, I worry about your observational skills, sometimes, considering that you are supposed to be a detective. The young lady is merely wearing black shoes with black stockings, something that happens all the time at school during winter."

Inspector Horace: "And I suppose you are going to tell me that she is actually wearing a skirt?"

Florence: "No, Father, her apron is her skirt."

Inspector Horace: "The restaurant is quiet this evening, which doesn't quite explain why we don't have more of the waiter's attention."

Florence: "Give him a chance, Father. I think he's new. And he may be delaying because Mother hasn't arrived yet. Oh my God, he's got our cutlery the wrong way round. You're not left-handed are you, Father? And I'm certainly not. And neither was Mother the last time I saw her stir the gravy. The fact that the waiter doesn't know his left from his right, might suggest that he's taken a wrong turn out of the kitchen, and then ended up somewhere other than the restaurant, even upstairs."

Inspector Horace: "Well, if he was working for me, he'd be on the list next to useless."

Florence: "That's a bit harsh, Father. The waiter just reminds me of someone waking up from an anaesthetic, that's all. Not that I wanted to remind you of your hernia operation. Oh look, there's Mother!"

Violet Horace walks in wearing a red dress that matches her husband's red scarf.

Violet Horace: "What a nice venue. Was it your choice, Florence?"

Florence: "Of course, Mother. Father's idea would have, according to internet feedback, taken us to a tiny hamlet, so unpopular that the tourist postcards have faded in the shop windows."

Violet Horace [*to her husband*]: "How was your day, dear?"

Inspector Horace: "Murder, as usual, Violet. How was your stocktake?"

Violet Horace: "It should have been completed sooner. Unfortunately, the horse had already jumped the stables and was half-way down the field."

Inspector Horace: "What on earth are you describing, Violet? Are you referring to the animal greetings cards that your boss sells?"

Violet Horace: "Someone has been stealing the greetings cards without paying for them. My boss kept me back to see if I had any ideas on how to stop it, being a detective's wife."

Inspector Horace: "Violet, the idea of you working, supposedly part-time, is not to create extra cases for me to have to investigate, but to help pay for our daughter's extravagances: that is dresses, not shoes, obviously."

[Florence's mother does not query the obviously, with her daughter's feet covertly hidden under the table.]

Florence: "Why would anybody want to steal a greetings card? You can just create one on a computer."

The waiter is now returning, still with the bulge in his pocket.

Waiter [*trying to appear family friendly*]: "Are you *guys* ready to order yet?"

Florence: "Only if it's the 5th of November. Although, by then, it will be nearly Christmas, and I will have missed all summer."

Waiter: "Sorry, I was being rather informal."

Florence: "Forgotten his script, more like [*In soliloquy*]. Don't bother questioning the formalities, Father – say yes to order, my stomach is starting to talk to me, and I've nearly lost my voice."

Inspector Horace: "In that case, my good waiter [*Florence laughs*], we are ready to order. And, starting with my wife, whose birthday it is, I know that she will want the wild mushroom omelette, as it is her favourite; and the wilder, the better [*Florence laughs again*]. For my daughter, who has turned vegan this evening, just the mushrooms. And, I will have the steak, medium-rare. For drinks, a coke for my daughter, adhering to her earlier specifications; a fresh orange juice for my wife, who drove herself here; and half a pint of bitter shandy with a dash of lime, for myself, so that I won't be over the limit, either."

Waiter: "All okay, sir, except the steak, which is rarer than you might think, because we don't actually have any."

Inspector Horace: "Perhaps roast chicken, instead?"

Waiter: "I'm afraid, sir, our meat supplier has let us down badly. The chicken hasn't even been given the opportunity to cross the Wyle Cop, let alone make it through the revolving doors [*Florence laughs*]."

Violet Horace: "This is no joke. To have run out of steak may be regarded as a misfortune; not to have any chicken, either, looks like carelessness."

Florence: "Mother, that sounds very 'Oscar Wilde'."

Waiter: "My apologies. Perhaps the wild mushrooms inside an omelette for you, too, sir? A change is as good as something different."

Florence [*in soliloquy*]: "Let's hope the food doesn't repeat on us like the waiter's use of language."

Inspector Horace: "You have enough mushrooms?"

Waiter: "We have plenty of room. As you can see, the restaurant is as large as it is capacious [*Florence laughs*]. I'll be back, soon. Time is as precious as it is valuable."

[*Florence laughs some more.*]

Florence [*with the waiter having disappeared again*]: "The waiter's use of language is interesting. He seems to repeat things by saying them again, only in a different way. Perhaps he's nervous, or maybe just forgetful. And that joke about the mushrooms was so Victorian. When the Victorian variety acts were performing here, they were probably telling the very same joke."

Inspector Horace: "So, Florence, what do you know about the Victorian acts that visited *The Lion Hotel* in Shrewsbury? I feel sure that my daughter has researched them."

Florence: "Well, I can inform you both that, over a period of three days in 1875, Professor Devono, for one, would have been performing his magic tricks to a presumably spellbound audience."

Inspector Horace: "How do you know this, Florence? Don't tell me, it was on the Internet."

Florence: "No, Father, not everything is available on the Internet. It was actually during a school trip to *Shropshire Archives* that I discovered a Victorian entertainments bill, which I asked to see and then photographed. I'll show you it on my phone. Look both, it says that between 28th October and 30th October 1875, the following acts were performed in the Assembly Room at *The Lion Hotel* in Shrewsbury, the room that is currently referred to as the Ballroom. To point out some of them to you, there is Alex Davis, the Premier Ventriloquist, which I think I said without moving my lips; Professor Devono, the magician that I've already mentioned; Miss Florence Wreghitt, the Great Lady Tenor and Comedienne, who is my namesake, of course; and Oliver Manley, R.A.M., who played the piano whilst blindfolded. I bet you couldn't do that, Father."

Inspector Horace: "I could, but to quote another variety act, Morecambe and Wise, I would be, 'Playing all the right notes. But not necessarily in the right order.'"

Florence: "You do that anyway, Father."

Inspector Horace: "It seems that my daughter really is a comedienne. Now tell us both more about Professor Devono, someone I feel sure that my daughter will know more about."

Violet Horace: "I wish I knew more about magic. It would be quite useful to learn how to make your father's red scarf (that he is even wearing on my birthday) disappear, and to make his liquorice habit invisible to the dentist."

Florence: "Well, I can't promise any of that, Mother, but I think you will both find this story as funny as it is hilarious. Apparently, Professor Devono, as he was known, had this trick where he used to make doves appear from a dove pan. However, when the lodging-house cat ate his doves, he used the cat instead for the trick, claiming that he had still produced the doves because they were inside the cat. Isn't that just the funniest thing to imagine, even for a vegan."

Inspector Horace: "Don't get any ideas about our cat, Florence. Tom still has nightmares from when you used to steal, I mean borrow, your mother's gold necklaces, and then place them around his neck."

Florence: "Only the best for our cat, Father. And just to show you the bottom of the entertainments bill, which was longer than today's posters, can you see how it says that the carriages will be arriving at 10.25? Doesn't that just allow us to imagine how it must have been? Father, you still use that term when you say to Mother that her carriage awaits, and she keeps you waiting until her make-up is just right. And providing further amusement for us reading it today, there is a cautionary notice which states that: 'All unseemly noises in the Hall are strictly prohibited.' I can't imagine how the boys in our class would manage – most of them would be thrown out as soon as they arrived."

Violet Horace: "Thank you for making my birthday so interesting, Florence. It makes such a difference when a venue has some history attached to it."

Florence: "We are in good company, Mother. And I think, between courses, I'm going to check out upstairs. Not only is there the suite where Charles Dickens stayed, but also the Adam Ballroom."

The waitress brings a tray of drinks.

Waitress: "I have some drinks for you. A coke for the young lady, the waiter remembered from an earlier conversation not to add in any ice or lemon. Then, there's a pure orange juice for you, madam, and a shandy for you, sir. The waiter will bring your meals over very soon. If the waiter seems a little odd, it's because a new set of guests have moved into the Dickens Suite. He always seems preoccupied and behaves oddly when that happens."

The waitress then makes her way to the other tables to check on them, before heading back out of the restaurant, as Violet Horace gives her apron a double-take.

Florence: "No, she isn't, Mother!"

Inspector Horace: "The Ballroom sounds as if it has religious connections, Florence."

Florence: "It's not Adam as in Adam and Eve, Father. It's Adam as in the style of the architecture used in the design of the Ballroom. It's an eighteenth-century neoclassical style that was adopted by Robert Adam and his brother, James."

Inspector Horace: "Is there anything that our daughter doesn't know?"

Florence: "How long the waiter is going to be. He seems to have disappeared completely, now. Perhaps he's related to Professor Devono. Oh, and I must tell you both about how, using a principle of magic, I managed to fool Mr Collins the other day at school. He was so mad that I had got the better of him."

Violet Horace: "What did you do, Florence? You know how your Father has said not to antagonise the man."

Florence: "Well, Mr Collins was convinced that I had turned up to school without shoes on, just in my stockings, with it being a cold day. As if I would do such a thing. School is a formal occasion, after all, when one must adhere to the school uniform policy, at least in part. I hadn't really been so daring, though I had merely chosen the vegan option. That is, of course, not leather shoes that shine in the light and make it obvious that you are wearing them, but suede shoes that make it less obvious. So, just like the waitress we talked about earlier, Father, the shoes blended perfectly with my black stockings. It was so funny to see Mr Collins' face, thinking that he had me, when, in fact, I had him. In magic, the same principle is used when an object painted black is juxtaposed against a black background in order to make it become invisible. It's only an illusion, really."

Violet Horace: "Isn't it amazing how the brain can be so easily fooled?"

Inspector Horace: "Annoying, too. If it wasn't for the criminal mind, my life would be made so much easier."

Florence: "If it wasn't for the criminal mind, Father, you could have retired by now. I worry, as a daughter, about the constant danger that you put yourself in."

Inspector Horace: "All in a day's work, Florence. And when I return to my office desk, the first thing that I look for is a picture of my daughter and wife, in that order."

[Violet Horace frowns.]
The waiter returns, still with the bulge in his pocket, and armed with two meals.

Waiter: "Your omelette, madam; your mushrooms, young lady; and yours to follow, sir."

Inspector Horace: "Can I ask if you are new to this job?"

Waiter: "What makes you say that, sir?"

Inspector Horace: "It is just that my daughter has pointed out to me that the cutlery was laid out the wrong way round as if we were all left-handers, which we are not."

Waiter: "I do apologise, sir, I'm always doing that. I learned my trade whilst looking in a mirror."

Inspector Horace: "And something else that is troubling my daughter, can you explain to me the bulge that is in your pocket, which I notice that you still have?"

Waiter: "Nothing to concern yourself with, sir. I'll return later to take your sweet orders. Enjoy your meals. I'm sure you will find them as tasty as they are appetising."

[Florence laughs at the fact tasty and appetising mean the same thing.]

Waitress: "And your meal, too, sir. Mushrooms always remind me of Christmas decorations. And, of course, Charles Dickens, who wrote *A Christmas Carol*, stayed here."

Inspector Horace: "You are very kind. I am quite relieved that your waiter didn't attempt to carry three plates."

Waitress: "Me, too. He finds juggling relationships hard enough."

Both the waiter and waitress make their way out of the restaurant with the waitress holding on to her apron string and making eyes at the waiter as she does.

Florence: "He doesn't seem to want to tell you what is in his pocket, Father. Don't you find that suspicious?"

Inspector Horace: "No more suspicious than the fact that he doesn't know which way round the cutlery should be, or that some of the words he uses just mean the same thing."

Florence: "Perhaps he's not a real waiter, although the waitress seems to know him well."

Inspector Horace: "Both thoughts had crossed my mind, too, Florence."

Violet Horace: "Well the cook is real; my omelette is just gorgeous."

Florence: "My mushrooms are tasty, too, Father. I wonder if the waiter will still have that bulge in his pocket next time *we* see him."

Inspector Horace: "Don't worry, Florence, I've got both eyes on him."

Florence: "The man on the table over there, presumably eating with his wife, has such a sad grin."

Inspector Horace: "How can you tell, Florence, he's wearing a beard?"

Florence: "No, not him, Father, the one on the table to the right of him, or is it to the left of him, whichever way you look at it. I'm sure the waiter wouldn't know."

Inspector Horace: "Perhaps the man has something on his mind."

Florence: "Don't you think it's odd that his wife isn't wearing anything around her neck?"

Violet Horace: "Perhaps she was in a rush to get in here, like I was."

Florence: "Perhaps!"

Inspector Horace [*still eating*]: "I think *The Lion Hotel* has converted me to vegan."

Violet Horace [*still eating*]: "The food is very nice."

Florence: "Mine was very nice, too. May I have permission to leave the table whilst you both finish off your meals? I'd like to take a look upstairs. It will give you both some alone time."

Inspector Horace: "In that case, a daughter may be excused."

Violet Horace [*seeing Florence stand up*]: "Florence, where on earth are your shoes?"

Florence: "Not you as well, Mother. I'm now a fully-fledged vegan, Father will explain."

Violet Horace: "I must admit to admiring the clear toenail varnish that you have used to fool your father. The red bottle you showed me the other day would clearly not have created the same illusion. And at least, once you are upstairs, you will look residential."

Florence: "Quite right, Mother. I couldn't have planned it better if my cover story had been premeditated. Nobody will now question why I am upstairs, but instead, think that I have strayed from one of the guest rooms out of entitled curiosity. At my leisure, I will be able to elegantly glide the entire length of the famous Adam Ballroom, before accidentally-on-purpose stumbling into the Dickens Suite. And once inside there, I plan on touching the ceiling with both hands, whether it leaves fingerprints or not; and to observe how 'the windows bulge out over the street, as if they were little stern-windows in a ship,' or perhaps a waiter's pocket; and all before finding again my elegant pose, which I shall use to lean over the 'queer old rail,' as Dickens did in 1858. Back soon, both."

Florence exits.

Violet Horace: "I do hope our daughter doesn't get herself into any trouble. I sometimes think that you let our daughter get away with murder."

Inspector Horace: "What trouble can Florence possibly get herself into. The Ballroom will probably be locked, and the Dickens Suite will more than likely be occupied by guests."

Violet Horace: "I'm sure you're right. Let her explore upstairs if she wants to. But why didn't you check that she had something on her feet when she got out of the car? I suppose she thinks it's some kind of joke to have birthday feet on my birthday."

Inspector Horace: "I didn't think to look. The way she walked didn't make it obvious that her soles were unprotected, as we climbed Wyle Cop together. I must admit that I was looking up at the tops of the buildings the whole of the time, and looking for the golden lion that Florence had described to me. I suppose I just thought that she had her pink shoes on. After all, they are practically the same colour as her skin."

Violet Horace: "Yes, and that's deliberate. Perhaps you can fetch them for her afterwards, or perhaps bring the car to the door when we are ready to leave. Do you think that the bare footprints that you found in the back garden the other day are Florence's, or from another intruder?"

Inspector Horace: "I don't know, but I think there is more to her desire to be that way than any kind of protest about leather. She is giving me all kinds of excuses when I catch her, including her strap has broken and she has taken the other shoe off in sympathy; that 'earthing' is good for her health; and that her soles making direct contact with the grass lawn helps her to absorb information better for important exams. And the time that she fetched my newspaper that way was followed up with no explanation at all."

Violet Horace: "Well, we can't complain about our daughter's mock results. She is making us very proud in that department."

Blackout

Act Two
Scene Two

Florence returns.

Florence: "Oh my God, the Ballroom was magnificent. The walls look just like a Wedgewood plate; and the chandeliers like something from a Cinderella movie. It is even domed like the buildings in the city you named me after. And the wooden floor is as smooth as ice cream, although not as cold, obviously. I passed the Dickens Suite, but I decided not to go in when I saw the waiter who has been serving us come out of there. Interestingly, Father, he no longer had a bulge in his pocket."

Inspector Horace: "My daughter is quite the detective. It would appear that whatever was in the waiter's pocket when he served us has been delivered to the Dickens Suite. I'm glad you were able to see the Ballroom, Florence. Perhaps they will let your mother and I dance in there, later."

Florence: "You must, both of you. It was like something from a fairy tale. The fact that the paintwork is worn and delicate will give you extra incentive not to bump into the walls as you dance."

Inspector Horace [*looking down at his daughter's feet*]: "You must have felt like Cinderella, Florence."

Florence: "Half right, Father, if you were thinking of after the ball. And whilst I was upstairs, I took the liberty of going to the toilet. I nearly didn't make it, though, the sign was so confusing. At first, I thought the room was TO LET."

Inspector Horace: "You mean that the letter 'I' was missing from the sign, Florence?"

Florence: "Father, I love our cryptic conversations."

Lady [*running through the restaurant and shouting*]: "HELP ME, SOMEONE, MY GOLD NECKLACE HAS BEEN STOLEN FROM MY ROOM."

Manager [*close behind and chasing the lady*]: "Madam, I'm sure that we can sort this out. Thefts from rooms are very rare; and from the Dickens Suite, unheard of."

Lady: "My husband and I were only away for ten minutes checking on our bill. The receptionist said that she would return but didn't, and the half-dressed waitress, who passed us by, said that we would have to wait for the receptionist."

Manager: "Well, the receptionist is back at her desk, now. Perhaps you could report all the details to her whilst I make some enquiries. Did you lock your room?"

Lady: "We didn't think to, being away for such a short time."

Manager [*nodding*]: "So, anybody could have stolen your necklace."

The manager is then seen having a word with the man with the beard.

Violet Horace: "I hope that you haven't made yourself a suspect, Florence?"

Florence: "Pray help me, Father. I don't want to go to prison. It will be in all the national newspapers, and after they have released me, I'll have to buy all my clothes from charity shops in order to take on somebody else's identity."

Inspector Horace: "Florence, innocent people don't go to prison."

End of Act Two

Act Three
Scene One

Florence prepares for the inevitable, nervously sinking her bare toe into the restaurant carpet's thin pile.

Inspector Horace: "Sit tight, Florence, the manager is returning and heading this way. I think the best way to play this is to look as innocent as possible."

Florence: "I don't think to look innocent will help. The bearded man was at the bottom of the stairs when I came down them, and has been telling tales to the manager."

Violet Horace: "I'll be surprised if we see the waiter again."

The manager arrives at Inspector Horace's table.

Manager: "I need to speak to your daughter, sir."

Inspector Horace: "Why would you need to speak to my daughter, it is my wife's birthday, and we haven't even been shown the dessert menu, yet?"

Florence: "It's no use, Father, it's like Mother says – I've inadvertently made myself a suspect. The lady was shouting that her necklace had been stolen, and I've not only been upstairs, but passed the very room it was stolen from."

Inspector Horace: "It will be fine, Florence. Most hotels have CCTV, and you are witness to the fact that you saw the waiter leaving the room in question. Just tell the manager, in your own words, what you saw."

Violet Horace: "This is turning into the usual kind of birthday, with my husband playing detective."

Inspector Horace: "I have no choice, Violet. Our daughter is about to be accused of theft, and other than her word, it may turn out that the only way I can prove her innocence is to solve the crime myself."

Manager: "Perhaps, sir, you and your daughter would like to accompany me to my office, where we can discuss this matter in private? In the meantime, your wife is free to order whatever her heart desires, as long as you pay for it later."

Violet Horace: "I won't order another thing until my daughter has been cleared of whatever it is, she is supposed to have done."

Florence: "Happy Birthday, Mother. Hope to be back, soon."

Inspector Horace: "Don't worry, Violet, I'll sort this out."

Violet Horace: "I hope so, or this will be another birthday to forget."

Blackout

Act Three
Scene Two

Florence, Inspector Horace, and the manager are now inside the manager's office. Inspector Horace has a look of concern. Florence is trying to maintain her look of innocence.

Manager: "Just confirm both of your names for me."

Inspector Horace: "I am Inspector Horace, no longer off duty; and this is my innocent daughter, Florence. She is currently at secondary school, so I must insist that I stay with her whilst you are asking her the questions. I would ask you not to contact the police station, as I will insist on taking the case, anyway."

Florence: "Father, I'm glad you're with me; and the best detective in your division."

Manager: "All I want is this lady's necklace back, and I will say no more about it, young lady, if you produce it for me, now. But I warn you, if you persist in pleading your innocence, I will have no option but to call the real police in."

Florence: "My Father is the real police, and I'm innocent."

Manager [*to Inspector Horace*]: "I should say now that the CCTV cameras haven't been working today, so we can only go on a first-hand witness account that describes your daughter making her way down the stairs without any shoes on."

Florence: "Oh great, that will be the bearded man, and I can't prove my innocence because the CCTV cameras haven't been working."

Manager: "The last thing I heard, our receptionist was still trying to make contact with the camera company, although she has been very busy."

Inspector Horace: "So, what evidence do you have to suggest that my daughter stole the necklace whilst she was upstairs?"

Manager: "As you must have noticed, being a detective, your daughter isn't currently wearing any shoes, and a pair of pink shoes have been found close to the room where the necklace was stolen from. It would seem, given the height of the heel, that your daughter removed them, perhaps when she was disturbed, in order to make a quick getaway from the scene of the crime. Without telling you your job, Inspector, all the evidence would point towards this."

Inspector Horace: "I have to inform you that my daughter hasn't been wearing shoes all evening, having left them in the car."

Florence: "Father, I have a confession to make."

Inspector Horace: "Florence, what do you need to tell me?"

Florence: "I didn't steal the necklace, but you won't be able to prove my innocence by finding my shoes in the car. I'm afraid I've misled you into thinking that I left them there. The truth is that I left them on the doormat at home, with my invisible socks inside them."

Manager: "It seems that your wayward daughter isn't averse to a few white lies. So, why should I believe her, now?"

Inspector Horace: "There is a world of difference between lying and not making something overtly clear. Why don't we see if the pair of shoes that you have found actually fit the feet of my daughter? If they don't, then you have no evidence, and she has to be declared innocent. Wouldn't you agree?"

Manager: "As you wish, sir. Let us pretend that your daughter is Cinderella, and test your theory out this instance, as it seems that we are not going to get a confession out of her; a daughter surely well-trained in how to avoid arrest, given her father's occupation."

Inspector Horace: "I'm not sure that I like the association you make between my occupation and my daughter's knowledge. Florence, be careful not to touch the sides of the shoes as you place your feet inside them. I don't want to disturb any fingerprints that might be on the sides. Toe prints we don't take, anyway."

Florence: "I can be careful, Father. At least a boy won't have had his feet inside them, presumably."

Manager: "I am sure that is the case, Miss. We don't have drag acts here all that often."

Florence: "Father, it's no use – the shoes are size six, as the label says, and fit me perfectly. They are even my favourite shade of pink."

Inspector Horace: "Oh, dear. Perhaps Florence, if you start by explaining to the manager why you couldn't have stolen the necklace?"

Florence: "Well, firstly, I don't have the necklace in my possession; secondly, I have no need for a gold necklace, because I no longer tease Tom our cat, by putting gold necklaces around his neck; and thirdly, I've never stolen anything in my life, except a few kisses from the boys, under mistletoe at Christmas time – and that was to raise money for a children's charity."

Manager: "This hardly proves the young lady's innocence. She could have stashed the necklace anywhere, intent on collecting it later; when the heat had died down in the restaurant, as well as in the kitchen. And then have plans to sell it to buy a dress; or perhaps some shoes."

Inspector Horace: "There is still something that you haven't told the manager, Florence; now is the time to tell him."

Florence: "It's just that I saw the waiter who served us in the restaurant leaving the Dickens Suite, where I overheard the lady had her necklace stolen from. He started serving us with a bulge in his pocket, but by the time he left the Dickens Suite, he no longer had the bulge. People don't lose weight that quickly, there was clearly something in his pocket."

Manager: "Unfortunately, Miss, we know all about the waiter's need to visit the room where the necklace was stolen from. He has his faults but has just the kindest heart. For each new guest that stays in the Dickens Suite, he places copies in the room of the letters that Charles Dickens wrote in 1838 and 1858. They would be what he had folded up inside his pocket."

Inspector Horace: "That would give him a reason for being in the room."

Florence: "This is hardly helping, Father."

Inspector Horace: "I'm thinking... Oh yes, whilst Florence was trying on the shoes, I happened to notice that they were actually brand new, and showed no signs of any wear. This would not suggest that they had been worn by someone who had earlier been wearing them. I parked the car some distance from your hotel. I think that we should still talk to your waiter, as even if he is not a suspect, he might have seen someone other than Florence, along that same corridor. He did seem to be missing a lot of the time this evening. I think that he may have had more on his mind than finding the time to deliver these letters to the Dickens Suite."

Manager: "In that case, I'll take your daughter back to the temporary care of her mother, and locate the waiter for you to question, Inspector."

Blackout

Act Three
Scene Three

The manager shows the waiter into his office, where Inspector Horace is waiting to question him.

Manager: "I will leave you to ask the questions, Inspector, but don't think for one minute that I have let your daughter off the hook. I have only returned her safely to her mother for the moment."

Inspector Horace: "It is much appreciated that you have allowed my daughter to sit with my wife, and let me reassure you that, like the diners we have detained to interview after your key staff, I will not be leaving this hotel until I have found your thief."

Waiter: "Did you enjoy your meal, sir?"

Inspector Horace: "It was very nice, but I need to ask you some questions concerning the theft of a lady's necklace this evening. You are an interesting character, there is no doubt, and there are one or two things that require clarification."

Waiter: "I'm innocent. Not guilty, even. I might not know my left from my right, but I know my right from my wrong."

Inspector Horace: "Perhaps you could explain to me, in your words, why you were seen leaving the Dickens Suite when surely you should have been downstairs serving in the restaurant. My daughter likened you to Lieutenant Columbo, the way you kept returning. And to return, you had to have disappeared in the first place."

Waiter: "I was delivering copies of the 'Two letters' that Charles Dickens wrote whilst he stayed at *The Lion Hotel* in Shrewsbury, to the latest guests staying in the Dickens Suite. I do this for everyone who stays there. On this occasion, they weren't in, but the door was left unlocked, so I just unfolded the letters from my pocket and deposited them amongst some magazines left on a chair."

Inspector Horace: "So, that was what you had in your pocket that was creating the bulge, that you thought did not concern me earlier. It seems that it has now become your alibi."

Waiter: "Yes, sir, that's right. I mean, correct."

Inspector Horace: "Either, right or correct would have sufficed. Now, can you confirm to the manager and I, that my daughter was without her shoes the whole evening, and didn't just take them off whilst upstairs, proving that the ones found near the Dickens Suite were not hers."

Waiter: "I'm afraid I didn't notice. I had other things on my mind, like how I was going to find time to deliver the copies of Dickens' letters whilst still serving in the restaurant. I like the guests to have them as soon as they move in. There had already been a delay because I hadn't realised that new guests had arrived."

Inspector Horace: "Okay, in that case, I think we are finished."

Waiter: "Sorry, I can't be of any help to your daughter. Her knowledge of Dickens was as impressive as it was remarkable."

Inspector Horace: "Do not concern yourself about it, now. We can't always notice everything. The fact is that you had reason to be in the Dickens Suite. It seems that I shall have to look elsewhere for my thief."

Manager: "What is your Plan B, Inspector?"

Inspector Horace: "I would like to just check on my daughter."

Manager: "As you wish, sir, but it isn't looking good for her, is it?"

Inspector Horace: "If I gave up that easily, I wouldn't be the best detective in my division, as my daughter alluded to, and is very proud of. With that in mind, I have no intention of letting her down. From my experience, the guilty party is never the most obvious, but in fact, the least. Excuse me while I just ingest a piece of liquorice to chew on for thought. I feel that I need one. What my dentist doesn't know won't hurt either of us."

Blackout

Act Three
Scene Four

Inspector Horace returns to his wife and daughter, with the manager chasing after him.

Florence: "Father, have you found the thief?"

Inspector Horace: "I'm afraid not, Florence."

Florence: "Then, I'm going to prison."

Violet Horace: "This can't be happening."

Inspector Horace: "No, Florence, I just need to think of the least obvious person who could have committed the crime."

Florence: "And the liquorice you're chewing on hasn't helped. Oh my God, Father, I know who it is. It's the receptionist."

Inspector Horace: "Explain your thinking, Florence, in as many words as necessary."

Manager: "Yes, I think your daughter better explain. Time is running out for her."

Florence: "Well, when I entered the hotel without anything on my feet, the receptionist asked me a strange thing. She asked me my shoe size and colour, despite not apparently being in a position to ever offer me anything from lost property, not that I wanted it. This not only gave her my shoe size, but the idea that a pink shoe would make it unclear as to whether I had been wearing shoes earlier on in the evening, or not. She also mentioned having a boyfriend who worked in a shoe shop. So, don't you see, Father, the receptionist not only knew my size but also had access to a shoe shop during the evening, when they would normally be closed. And with this opportunity, she was able to plant shoes outside the Dickens Suite that would fit me afterwards. She also knew because the manager had her dealing with it, that the CCTV cameras were not working, and that I would have no way of proving for definite that I had started the evening without shoes. The receptionist may even have delayed the camera company fixing the camera in order to allow time for her to carry out the theft of the necklace. By choosing the Dickens Suite as the place to steal from, suspicion upon herself was further reduced in creating another suspect, the kind-hearted waiter who liked to drop off copies of Charles Dickens' letters to guests staying in the Dickens Suite. And did you see the cheeky glance that the waitress gave the waiter? What if, the waiter had promised the receptionist a 'thousand kisses', to quote Dickens' letter of 1838, to then later succumb to the temptations of the waitress. This would give the receptionist an added motive to commit the crime, other than a financial one, given that she would be adding the waiter to the list of suspects. And, of course, who better than the receptionist to know all the movements of the guests; such as, when a room has been left unoccupied. And if locked, has access to the master key. The receptionist would have been able to time her moment to steal the necklace to perfection. And, for the record, I believe that the husband sitting at the table with the lady who wasn't wearing a necklace is innocent of that particular crime. He was just too mean to buy his wife a necklace."

Inspector Horace: "And, of course, we now know that the receptionist kept the lady and her husband waiting when they just wanted to check their bill, to then not return. This would be when she carried out the theft. Florence – you have solved the case."

Manager: "Your daughter, Inspector, is something special, and I feel guilty for having ever accused her."

Inspector Horace: "And so is your hotel. And that has come out of the mouth of my quick-witted and intelligent daughter, whose outward appearance has deceived us all."

Manager: "You must return under better circumstances, Inspector. At our expense, you must, with your wife, stay in the Dickens Suite and look across at the crooked houses."

The manager then returns to his office to call the police. Meanwhile, Inspector Horace and his wife and daughter pass reception, not letting on to the surprised receptionist what her fate will be. Florence leaves how she arrived, with the gorgeous pink shoes that were found having to be bagged as evidence.

End of Act Three

Act Four
Scene One

It is the following day at school, and whilst waiting for the teacher to arrive, Florence is questioned by her best friend, Amelia about her mother's birthday.

Amelia [*rearranging her school bag whilst talking*]: "Did you have a nice time yesterday evening, Florence?"

Florence: "I've had better evenings, even with homework to do. Can you believe, I was accused of stealing?"

Amelia: "Stealing what? The limelight?"

Florence: "It's not funny, Amelia, the hotel manager accused me of stealing a necklace from a lady's room, and the Dickens Suite of all rooms."

Amelia: "And your father had greater expectations of you?"

Florence: "My father has no expectations of me, not after the last school report."

Amelia: "What did it say? You never showed me."

Florence: "It was more what it didn't say. My father is a detective, after all."

Mr Old: "Girls. Talking?"

Florence: "Sorry, sir, I didn't know you'd arrived, or I would have made even more noise." [*Everyone laughs.*]

Mr Old: "Well, I'm here now. I'm afraid my car gave up the ghost this morning."

Florence: "Which ghost was that? The one who starts the car? Well, you're here now, anyway." [*More laughter is heard.*]

Amelia [*in sotto voce*]: "Florence, do you enjoy winding our history teacher up the wrong way?"

Florence [*to Amelia in sotto voce*]: "Like a toy. I can't help it; he reminds me of an older version of Judge Rinder."

Amelia [*in sotto voce*]: "Then it seems you can't avoid the law."

Mr Old [*in voce forte*]: "Today, we are going to talk about historic Shrewsbury."

Florence: "I was there last night, sir."

Mr Old: "Then, you can start us off, Florence."

Florence: "What am I starting us off with, sir? You'll have to be more specific." [*Everyone laughs.*]

Mr Old: "Well, tell us a fact you know about Shrewsbury."

Florence: "Okay, well to combine History and English Literature together, as much as it will confuse the boys, Charles Dickens stayed at *The Lion Hotel*."

Kevin [*shouting from the desk behind Florence*]: "That's obvious. That is why they have a room called the Dickens Suite."

Florence: "And did you know, Kevin, that Dickens stayed there in 1838 and 1858. And on Thursday, 12th August 1858, described 'the crookedest black and yellow old houses, all manner of shapes except straight shapes.' Not unlike your nose after the rugby accident. And no wonder, playing with a ball shaped like a banana." [*Everyone laughs.*]

Mr Old: "So, Kevin, what historical buildings or objects do you know of in Shrewsbury, if any?" [*Florence smiles.*]

Kevin: "I happen to know that inside *The Buttermarket*, in Howard Street, Shrewsbury, there is a large organ hidden away."

Florence [*in sotto voce*]: "The best place for them."

[*Amelia is struggling to contain her laughter, thinking that Florence is making a boy reference.*]

Amelia [*in sotto voce*]: "I love that place, though. Despite it primarily being a nightclub for the over eighteens, which obviously I am not, the toilets are hilariously labelled for 'Girls' and 'Boys'." [*Florence smiles at Amelia saying 'Girls' first.*]

Mr Old [giving the girls a disapproving stare for talking]: "Go on, Kevin."

Kevin: "It's a Mighty Wurlitzer Theatre Organ. It dates to 1936, has three manuals, now ten ranks of pipes, sides that change colour, and used to be played at the Ritz Cinema in Chatham, Kent before the Shropshire Theatre Organ Trust acquired it in the eighties."

Colin [*from the other side of class*]: "Organ music puts me to sleep."

Amelia: "My gran goes to listen to it, and she doesn't fall asleep." [*Florence smiles.*]

Florence: "In Kevin's defence, although I'd rather defend a goal in rugby, the organ at *The Buttermarket* has a sound of its very own. Not only do the chambers contain 708 pipes, they also house real percussion instruments. When the organist puts his foot on the swell pedal, the shutters open to reveal its magnificent sound. And when the organist 'waterfalls' between all three manuals, it is a sight to behold. Colin, it seems your glasses are a sign of intelligence, after all." [Everyone claps.]

Mr Old: "Thank you, Kevin. And thank you, Florence, for your second contribution, which was in a strange way in support of Kevin. And thank you, Colin, for your small contribution."

Florence: "Pleasure."

[*Kevin remains silent, which usually means that he is up to something, and Colin has nothing else to say.*]

Mr Old: "Class dismissed early. I need to sort my car out with the garage."

[*The classroom then empties, leaving just Florence and Amelia.*]

Amelia [*observing Florence looking under her desk*]: "What's the matter, Florence?"

Florence: "I can't find one of my shoes."

Amelia: "I thought you knew not to take them off when there are boys behind us. You know how they like to play tricks on us. And in summer, when you have no tights on, it is surely just too risky. One girl they chased and caught up with had to walk practically all the way to school without anything on her feet."

Florence: "Well, I wish the boys' tricks would involve disappearing themselves."

Amelia: "What are you going to do, Florence? The boy responsible has obviously left, they all have. And the teacher, too. Not that Mr Old would have any reason to help you, you are so cheeky to him."

Florence: "The dear old man has a soft spot for me, really. And I for him."

Amelia: "Just an understanding, I would have thought."

Florence: "My destiny is going to be that I will have to hop for the rest of the day. It will not be Kevin who has taken my shoe, he would never hold such a grudge, however badly I treated him. It must have been the other boy, Mark, for amusement. He was the next closest to me. I'm almost flattered that he should single me out for such a prank, and could almost fancy him for it if he wasn't a boy."

Amelia: "What are you saying, Florence, you prefer a lioness to a lion? You had better keep that one to yourself."

Florence: "I'm not scared of either kind of relationship."

Amelia: "Please don't name me if you are thinking of coming out."

Florence: "Don't worry, Amelia, like straight relationships, one needs to love the person."

Amelia: "Don't you love me, Florence?"

Florence: "Like, not love, there's a difference."

Amelia: "So, what would I have to do to make you love me, Florence?"

Florence: "You would have to sacrifice your right shoe for me."

Amelia: "You mean, give you my right shoe, whilst I went without?"

Florence: "No, silly, we are a different size. You would merely be going without it as well to show solidarity."

Amelia: "Then, we would both be caught hopping."

Florence: "Not if we were careful. Don't you feel like showing the boys that we are tougher than them? That their pranks cannot hurt us. That the stones on the concrete don't bother us, the insects on the grass are merely there to tickle us, and to be self-conscious is to care."

Amelia: "I'm sorry, Florence, I can't risk getting caught without my shoe. I've been in enough trouble over my uniform this term. And if the head teacher should find the other shoe in my bag, I wouldn't even have the excuse that a boy had stolen it."

Florence: "I was only playing with you, Amelia. I value our friendship too much to ask such a thing of you."

Amelia: "Are you really going to hop for the rest of the day?"

Florence: "Of course not, Amelia. According to Miss Demeanour, our PE teacher, my balance is hopeless, so I shall have to forget the other shoe in sympathy and just go without both for the rest of the day, until the time the boy thinks it's only right to return the missing shoe to my foot. There is no way I am going to let the boys think that I am a bit bothered by their actions."

Amelia: "That's the spirit, Florence. My sister takes hers off after a night out, not a bit bothered about what anyone thinks. Although, she has usually had too much alcohol to drink by then. It does rather take away her ability to care."

Florence: "Amelia, assuming that none of the teachers has consumed any alcohol, although doubtful in the geography teacher's case, the way he thought that America was part of Europe the other day, you will need to provide cover for me every time we see a teacher, and protection every time you see a boy. This will involve, for you, standing in front, or to the side, or even behind me, whilst I am on the move, and then letting me use your bag, as well as mine, to disguise my feet, whilst sitting at my desk."

Amelia [*With a concerned face as she and Florence make their way to the next class early, having avoided going outside*]: "Be careful, Florence, you aren't even wearing any socks."

Florence [*Displaying a brave face but aware of her predicament*]: "I know and being without shoes always seems to get me into trouble."

Amelia: "When else has it got you into trouble, apart from at school, which I know about?"

Florence: "*The Lion Hotel.* It was how I made myself a suspect."

Amelia: "What happened at the hotel, Florence?"

Florence: "Surely, when I said earlier that I was accused of theft, you didn't think that I had been caught red-handed, it was pink-soled."

Amelia: "So, you did steal the necklace, Florence? Your father must be so disappointed in you."

Florence: "Of course not. My lack of footwear merely made me a suspect. The staff had not noticed me that way before the theft, and with a bearded man making it worse, it was thought that I had left a pair of shoes by the Dickens Suite, where the theft took place, before making my escape. It turned out the shoes were planted, and the receptionist had set me up."

Amelia: "That's awful, Florence."

Florence: "Don't worry, Amelia, I worked it out. Not that I should have had to, with a father who is a detective."

Amelia [*in admiration*]: "You have a brilliant mind, Florence. Really pretty. And easy to talk to."

Florence: "Okay, don't overdo it, Amelia."

Both girls somehow make it safely to the next class, before anyone else. Meanwhile, morning break time continues outside for everyone else.

Blackout

Act Four
Scene Two

With Florence and Amelia already in the classroom, the teacher arrives, followed by the rest of the class, half girls and half boys. The compulsory subject, one that was sure to be over-subscribed, if not always fully attended.

Amelia [*in sotto voce*]: "Just pray, Florence, you are not called to the front of the class to collect and deliver the handouts, like last time we were in English. If the teacher doesn't notice your predicament, the boys, if they don't know it already, surely will."

Miss Charles: "Welcome everyone, it is nice to see every desk filled, today, even if it isn't the flu season."

Florence [*in sotto voce*]: "Miss Charles should be on the stage. Except that he, I mean she, would probably be dazzled by the lights."

Amelia [*in sotto voce*]: "Florence, you're so funny. Do you think Miss Charles really needs those dark glasses?"

Florence [*in sotto voce*]: "I suspect they are just so that she doesn't have to look at us."

Amelia [*in sotto voce*]: "It might work in your favour, Florence." [*Florence smiles*]

Miss Charles: "Bear with me class, I just want to check over my PowerPoint slides, to make sure that they are error-free. Talk amongst yourselves."

Florence [*in sotto voce*]: "It's a bit late to be checking them, now."

[*As Florence says it, and with the teacher's back turned, a paper aeroplane lands near to Florence and Amelia's desk. But before Florence can pick it up, Miss Charles turns around and somehow manages to see it.*]

Miss Charles: "What have we here? A billet-doux, perhaps? I shall read it out aloud, it was presumably meant for someone. 'Meet me by the gnarled oak tree at lunchtime, my Cinderella, it will be a match made in heaven.' My goodness, whoever it was can spell. That narrows it down. Is anyone going to admit to it?"

Florence: "Nobody is going to own up, Miss. It was obviously a boy, as they like aeroplanes, and meant for me, despite falling short. If I manage to work out who it is, I might show up to give them flying lessons." [*Everyone laughs.*]

Miss Charles [*smiling*]: "Then, you have an admirer, Florence. Now, if you will excuse me, class, I seem to have the wrong memory stick. I'll just need to fetch the correct one from my office."

[*This prompts a tumultuous noise to be heard before Miss Charles can even make it through the classroom door, as the whole class try and converse at the same time. Still to be heard, though, are the conversations between Amelia and Florence, which continue after their teacher has left.*]

Amelia: "Who do you think the bad shot was, Florence, I wasn't looking?"

Florence: "It was Mark, who is now to the side of us, rather than behind us. Moving desks has made him even more of a suspect than if he had stayed where he was."

Amelia: "So, it's Mark who has your shoe. Who would have thought? And he seemed the only sensible one. Given that it is sensible Mark, surely, he wouldn't risk having your shoe inside his bag, to be found in the event of a search, or even inside his locker. You are going to have to meet him at lunchtime, as the note says, if you want your shoe back to walk home in. And the gnarled oak tree, of course, is down the bottom of the field. At the very bottom of the field."

Florence: "Okay, Amelia, I get the imagery. Anyway, I shall not be meeting him. I would rather walk home barefoot."

Amelia: "You might have to, Florence. Perhaps it is what you want, anyway. Maybe you and Mark have staged the whole thing together to get one up on shoeless Melissa, who had stolen the part of Cinderella from you in the school play. Or is it for some other misguided reason?"

Florence: "Amelia, what do you take me for? Anyway, Melissa isn't here today, she has caught a cold. She should have chosen a warmer day to persuade Mr Collins of her suitability for the play."

Amelia: "Well, you seem to have created the situation for yourself at *The Lion Hotel* and made your shoes rather too available for Mark to steal. Unless, of course, Mark is making a romantic gesture. Perhaps you should meet him by the gnarled oak tree, after all, and wearing just your left shoe so that he can return the other shoe to your foot as if he were Prince Charming."

Florence: "You know, your last theory might just be right, Amelia. Perhaps Mark does fancy me. He is the best prospect out of the whole class."

Amelia: "So, you do like boys, after all, Florence, and you were just winding me up earlier about preferring your own kind, romantically. It's not that there is anything wrong with it. Boys can be horrible, after all. Katy Perry kissed a girl, even if it was only a song lyric. And my sister did it for a dare."

Florence [*smiling*]: "I admit that I was winding you up, like my father's old pocket watch. You can now take one deep breath, instead of two."

Amelia: "Is your father old-fashioned?"

Florence: "Very. He is worse than our head teacher. He thinks that my skirt should reach my ankles at least."

Amelia: "Well, it has a long way to go."

Florence: "I know, bless him. But, today, it might have been useful to have risked being tripped up by it, and have it touch the floor. What one cannot see, nobody can be worried about."

[*Miss Charles is now returning.*]

Miss Charles: "Okay, well I've found the memory stick, so we can now begin the lesson."

Amelia [*in sotto voce*]: "About time. We do go to school to learn, don't we?"

Florence [*in sotto voce*]: "I love Miss Charles, a thousand times over. She gives us time to have a conversation and one that has nothing to do with English, although it is obviously in English. I can't bear her French lessons. When are we ever going to need that?"

Amelia [*in sotto voce*]: "If we go on holiday to France?"

Florence [*in sotto voce*]: "You won't see me stuck in that tunnel. It would be worse than walking through a subway at night, which my father says I should never do alone. And if Miss Charles should ever dare to venture into the canteen, she might consider teaching us Greek, the number of plates that find themselves smashed on the floor." [*Amelia looks at Florence and smiles, having Greek relatives.*]

Miss Charles [*looking straight at Florence and Amelia*]: "Girls, we have started."

Amelia: "Sorry, Miss."

Florence: "Sorrier still, Miss." [*Amelia gives Florence a short stare, unable to believe how she could outdo her like that.*]

Miss Charles: "For your cheek, Florence, you can hand out the leaflets again this week."

[*Amelia smiles, wondering how Florence will manage it without her non-regulation school feet being discovered.*]

Florence [*half looking at the teacher, and half smiling at Mark*]: "I've twisted my ankle, Miss."

Miss Charles: "Then you may be excused, Florence. Amelia can hand out my leaflets, instead. I certainly want them handed out, given that I have stuck my neck out photocopying them, with secondary school finances such as they are."

[*Amelia smiles at Florence as she hands a leaflet to her, and Miss Charles ends up walking around the room, anyway, to discover Florence trying to hide her feet from everyone.*]

Miss Charles [*just to Florence*]: "Oh, you poor thing. But do not forget to return shoes to your feet for your lunchtime break. I say that because the trouble with common sense is that not everyone has it."

Florence [*although knowing it to be only half impossible*]: "Of course, Miss. I wouldn't want to put my foot in it with the head teacher."

Miss Charles: "And, Florence, after having a rather fascinating, if not rather outdated conversation with Mr Old, I understand that you are a Charles Dickens fan, so you will be particularly interested in my presentation on *Oliver Twist*."

Florence: "Yes, Miss. Charles Dickens portrays poverty so well and makes us all thankful for the shoes on our feet."

[*Florence makes eye contact with Mark, not unnoticed by Amelia.*]

Miss Charles: "So, as Florence is bound to know the answer to my next question, I think I will ask you, Kevin. The question is, which quotation do we most associate with the character of Oliver?"

[*Kevin hesitates despite the simplicity of the question.*]

Miss Charles: "I'm going to have to hurry you, Kevin. After all, he who hesitates never has a second thought."

Kevin: "Please, sir, I want some more."

Mark: "Shoes."

[*Says Mark to finish the sentence, causing Florence to smile, thinking that their meeting at the gnarled oak tree must be on for lunchtime.*]

Miss Charles: "Kevin, you were quite correct. Mark, I think you will find that Oliver was looking for more gruel, although, of course, he was also in want of shoes."

[*Miss Charles then flicks through her slides before closing the lesson, with everyone by the end knowing as much about Oliver Twist as the Christmas movie had taught them.*]

Blackout

Act Four
Scene Three

Florence makes her way to the gnarled oak tree down the bottom of the school field, wearing just one shoe, and hoping, or perhaps hopping, that Mark will be there to meet her.

Florence: "Amelia, shield me from prying eyes."

Amelia: "Happy to be your knight in shining armour until Prince Charming takes over."

Florence: "Much appreciated, Amelia. The concrete is a little rough, and grass I am sure will be ticklish, but I shall manage the walk."

Amelia: "Just imagine that you are on the paving slabs and grass at home, Florence. I bet your father mows the grass in perfect strips like a tennis court."

Florence: "You know he does, Amelia, you've been to my house."

Amelia: "Well, the tree is appearing closer, now that we have made it to the edge of the grass. I just wonder what time Mark calls lunchtime, or even if he still intends on meeting you. The looks you gave him may not be enough to convince him that you think it is still on."

Florence: "Mark seems nice, so he is hardly likely to keep me waiting. Anyway, I will only wait so long."

Amelia: "How can he be nice, Florence, he's taken away your shoe. In your father's eyes that would be theft, and the very thing you were wrongly accused of at *The Lion Hotel*."

Florence: "I didn't think of it like that. I shall have to keep this quiet from, Father if I do ever bring Mark home."

Amelia: "I think he's stood you up, anyway, Florence, unless he is just stuffing his face in the canteen, without a single concern for you."

Florence: "Then, how is Mark planning to return my shoe to me?"

Amelia: "Maybe he'll throw it to you like the aeroplane."

Florence: "Hopefully not, he'll surely miss. But he will think of a way, I feel sure."

Amelia: "Maybe you have Mark completely wrong, Florence. Perhaps he was never intending on returning your shoe and it is a cruel prank. The wrong sort, as your father would put it."

Florence: "Perhaps I am not as good a judge of character as my father. Oh my God, the ants are out. Hundreds of them."

Amelia: "Try and avoid them, Florence. I feel for you, I really do. Is that the head teacher coming towards us? If it is, you'll have more to worry about than a few ants."

Florence: "A few ants, Amelia, it's a whole ants' nest and they're now crawling all over my feet."

Amelia: "They're not stinging ants, though. They are just like the ones we had in the science lab."

Florence: "No, they're not stinging ants."

Amelia: "You're still brave, Florence. Most girls would scream."

Florence: "I can't now. If the head teacher was to hear me, he would know something was up. But he's still heading towards us. What does he want? You'll have to try and distract him, Amelia."

Amelia: "How will I do that?"

Florence: "Talk to him and take the conversation back to the hockey pitch."

Amelia: "I'll do my best, Florence."

Unbeknown to Florence, her shoe is inside a waste bin inside the school grounds. It seems that Mark has had second thoughts and panicked.

End of Act Four

Act Five
Scene One

Inspector Horace is on a later start, whilst his wife is enjoying a day off in her dressing gown.

Inspector Horace: "Work is calling."

Violet Horace: "I didn't hear the telephone ring."

Inspector Horace: "Just an expression, dear."

Violet Horace: "Before you go, what did you think of our daughter's antics yesterday evening?"

Inspector Horace: "I was proud of our daughter. I couldn't have solved the case better myself."

Violet Horace: "I was referring to her rather unintelligent footwear choice."

Inspector Horace: "I don't recall our daughter having made any kind of footwear choice."

Violet Horace: "Must you play with words. Surely, that should be left to the criminal trying to explain their innocence."

Inspector Horace: "They don't have many to play with. Just 'no' and 'comment'."

Violet Horace: "You are too soft on our daughter."

[As his wife says it, Inspector Horace takes a couple of pieces of liquorice from his packet to chew on as food for thought. He only wishes he could get his wife interested in it, as it would avoid many a sticky conversation. And, at the same time, he is trying to put on the trusty red scarf that he always wears, whatever the weather.]

Inspector Horace: "I must go. I cannot expect the Chief Inspector to always be on the golf course when I am late."

Violet Horace: "And then, you might miss your tea, too, or whatever it is that Amy seems to make a better cup of, at the police station than I as your wife apparently do."

Inspector Horace: "Your play on words in relation to a golf tee is an interesting one, Violet, except it is a coffee that Amy makes for me. Which might, in some way, explain why I prefer hers."

Violet Horace: "Well, drive carefully, dearest, not at the speed police training has taught you."

Inspector Horace: "Bidding you a leisurely afternoon, Violet."

[Inspector Horace then drives to the police station as if displaying a blue light.]

Blackout

Act Five
Scene Two

Inspector Horace has now made it through the door at the police station. It is a heavy one but still not half as difficult as negotiating a revolving one.

Inspector Horace: "Good afternoon, Amy. How is my favourite police receptionist?"

Amy [*looking down at Inspector Horace's scarf*]: "In the same position as your favourite sweet."

Inspector Horace [*smiling and removing the piece of liquorice stuck to his scarf*]: "What are you stuck on, Amy?"

Amy: "The one computer screen."

Inspector Horace: "You know I can't help you with that."

Amy: "Don't you inspectors go on advanced computer courses, as you go on advanced everything else?"

Inspector Horace: "Amy, to get on an advanced computer course, I would have to have seen the email about the basic computer course."

Amy: "Perhaps your daughter could help you with the basics. I heard that she solved the case for you last night when she found herself accused of a necklace theft."

Inspector Horace: "Yes, that was slightly embarrassing."

Amy: "From what I have heard, not that I listen to gossip, many other aspects of the evening must have been equally embarrassing."

Inspector Horace: "Can you be more specific, Amy? I think I should know what is being said about me behind my back. After all, that is the only time I won't know about it."

Amy: "Some people are saying that, as a detective, you should have been more observant than not to notice your daughter's lack of footwear. Others are saying that you must have noticed but had no control over your daughter to do anything about her rebellious behaviour. Whatever it is, Florence is rebelling against."

Inspector Horace: "For the record, Amy, I was looking at the tops of the historic buildings along Wyle Cop. Whilst my wife might look at the bottom half for the shops, I prefer looking at the top halves of them. It costs nothing to look."

Amy: "Quite the historian, Inspector Horace. You are welcome around my Victorian home any day. It becomes quite cosy around my cold cast iron fireplace at night."

Inspector Horace: "Well, that is an offer I might find difficult to decline. I like nothing more than to see flames in the right setting. That is, not ones created by an arson attempt."

[Amy, judging by her expression, hopes that he will one day visit.]

Amy *[in a nervous voice, never knowing when she has said too much]*: "Then, don't decline. You would be ever so welcome. Very welcome, even."

Inspector Horace: "What is the difference between the two, Amy. You remind me of the waiter from *The Lion Hotel*, who would say the same thing twice in one sentence. My daughter picked up on it straight away."

Amy: "There is no difference, you are just extremely welcome, that is all."

[Inspector Horace smiles at Amy, having inadvertently created a third alternative with the same meaning, for being made welcome at her home.]

Inspector Horace: "Well, if we add coffee to the arrangement, it will be sooner rather than later, Amy."

Amy [*blushing and changing the subject*]: "I cannot believe that your daughter rescued herself from being arrested last night. I think if I had a father that was a detective, I would expect him to have solved the case first. And it is almost like your daughter made herself a suspect so that she was provided with the challenge of proving herself innocent, although obviously, she didn't. Of course, she didn't."

Inspector Horace: "Don't rub it in, Amy. Although, if it was an ointment, it would be very welcome."

Amy: "Do you have a bad back, Inspector Horace?"

Inspector Horace: "Only after carrying my wife's shopping."

[*Amy smiles, always finding his wife jokes funny. She knows he doesn't mean them with any malice. Not really.*]

Amy: "What did you think of *The Lion Hotel* as a venue? Last time I was there, the lion above the door scared me half to death."

Inspector Horace: "You really should control your alcohol intake, assuming it was just alcohol you had taken."

Amy: "Inspector Horace, are you trying to suggest that I was as stoned as the lion? Any drugs that I take are prescription only."

Inspector Horace: "Yes, and the instructions always say not to consume alcohol whilst on the tablets."

Amy: "I do know what the pharmacist confirmed. But what my pharmacist doesn't know, will not hurt him any more than what your dentist doesn't know."

Inspector Horace: "My dentist doesn't see the value in liquorice's other properties, whereas drugs in the wrong hands can be dangerous."

Amy: "How can liquorice make anyone think?"

Inspector Horace: "The secret, Amy, is in the fact that you cannot talk and eat it at the same time. And whilst I am not talking, I am thinking."

Amy: "I get it, now. You have never explained it like that to me before. Chocolate helps me forget loneliness."

Inspector Horace: "Have you still not found a willing partner?"

Amy: "They're all too young for me. I like a mature man with intellect."

Inspector Horace: "Then, the right man might be closer than you think."

Amy: "I know he is."

Inspector Horace: "Where is the Chief Inspector, Amy?"

Amy: "I'm the last person to know."

Inspector Horace: "Then, he's on the golf course again."

Amy: "Quite possibly. The last time, when I wasn't on a shift, he asked me to caddy for him, but I declined because I believe that I mollycoddle him enough at the police station."

Inspector Horace: "Do you feel you have to mollycoddle me, Amy?"

Amy [*blushing*]: "Yes, but I love mollycoddling you."

Inspector Horace: "That is nice to hear. A coffee at your usual temperature and strength would be most welcome."

Amy: "I'll be into your office with it soon."

Blackout

Act Five
Scene Three

With hardly time for the kettle to have boiled, Amy, in stocking feet, brings Inspector Horace his favourite drink.

Inspector Horace: "Why have you placed my coffee that side of the desk, Amy?"

Amy: "Because your mouse is the other side, and I am pretty sure it has been in that exact same position since the computer was delivered."

Inspector Horace: "The mouse is that side because I am right-handed, Amy. The fact that I don't use it is irrelevant. And, worryingly, like the waiter at *The Lion Hotel*, you do not seem to realise that the lion's share of the earth's population display right-handedness."

Amy: "Apologies, Inspector Horace, I do now remember you saying that there were more left-handed criminals than right-handed ones. I didn't mean to imply that you were one."

Inspector Horace: "Indeed. Left-handedness is not an affliction that a man wants, or even needs to possess, and should he find himself with it, should consider using his right hand at every opportunity."

Amy: "The new Chief Inspector, who starts next week, is left-handed."

[*Inspector Horace nearly spills his coffee all over the computer.*]

Inspector Horace: "Where are your shoes, Amy?"
Amy: "In my car, Inspector Horace."

Inspector Horace: "Have you gone without shoes on purpose today, Amy, to perhaps check my observational skills? After all, black shoes and black tights do not always make it obvious as to whether shoes are being worn. Florence explained to me at *The Lion Hotel*, how black upon black, as if by magic, appears invisible. However, Amy, you forget that your shiny leather shoes make it more obvious when you are not wearing shoes. Although, I understand why you wear them so shiny. It is, of course, so that you can use them as a mirror to check your make-up. And very nice it still looks."

Amy: "You have found me out, Inspector Horace. Why didn't you say straight away that you had noticed my lack of footwear? The Chief Inspector would have done so if he had been around."

Inspector Horace: "I was playing the game back, Amy. Now, make sure you put some on soon, as the retiring Chief Inspector's golf game won't last forever. Unless, of course, he stays inside the nineteenth hole."

Amy [*coming clean*]: "I will, they're only under my desk. These tights are thin, and I'm not so brave as Florence to have walked across the car park without them."

Inspector Horace: "Oh, you might not know this, as it wasn't relevant to the case, but my wife was late for her own birthday, despite working in a greetings card shop."

Amy: "Your wife would be just getting her own back for all the times you were working late here, I imagine."

Inspector Horace: "I suspect that you are right, Amy. Cold lasagne is obviously my clue."

Amy: "If you were mine, or I yours, Inspector Horace, I would make sure that your food was warm, as I would the fire."

Inspector Horace [*handing over his empty mug*]: "Well, that is very thoughtful of you, Amy."

[*Amy then tiptoes out of Inspector Horace's office, holding the mug.*]

Blackout

Act Five
Scene Four

Amy, after returning to her desk, and making herself Chief Inspector ready, receives a telephone call to put through to Inspector Horace.

Inspector Horace: "Who is it and what is it, Amy?"

Amy: "It's the manager of *The Lion Hotel*."

Inspector Horace: "What on earth does he want?"

Amy: "Exactly that. He has discovered money missing from the safe, and as he has met you already, would like you to be the one to investigate the theft. The second one in as many days."

Inspector Horace: "That is not exactly the kind of crime a man in my position should be investigating, but as he insists, and as there have been no lifeless bodies discovered by dogs this morning, I shall take the call. At least it's not Florence's head teacher pretending to know everything."

Amy: "Thank you, Inspector Horace. It is not like he was about to take *no* for an answer."

[Amy puts the call through.]

Manager: "Is that Inspector Horace's phone?"

Inspector Horace: "Inspector Horace at the other end of it."

Manager: "I assume that your receptionist has already explained my reason for calling."

Inspector Horace: "Amy has, and I must ask, has your receptionist returned?"

Manager: "She is still with you, as far as I am aware, and will not be welcome back here."

Inspector Horace [*wondering why Amy hasn't told him such an important thing*]: "I'll check, and then subject to traffic, will arrive at your hotel shortly."

Manager: "Much appreciated, and apologies again for yesterday evening's misunderstanding."

Inspector Horace: "Subsequent apology accepted."

[*Inspector Horace then makes his way to Amy before the receiver has hardly had a chance to hit the holder of his red telephone.*]

Amy: "I know, I forgot to mention that the hotel receptionist is still in custody. She assaulted a police officer with her shoe whilst she was being arrested and had her shoes bagged up in evidence, as the ones found by the Dickens Suite were. She is waiting for her mother to bring her another pair."

Inspector Horace: "Shoes, shoes and more shoes. Nothing but trouble for all the money that they cost. It is no wonder Florence doesn't bother with any."

Inspector Horace leaves the police station, wearing the red scarf that he has never taken off, hoping it will bring him luck, given that it would appear he now has to solve a theft all by himself.

Blackout

Act Five
Scene Five

Inspector Horace arrives at The Lion Hotel, taking care not to end up in the same section of the revolving door as the lady in front of him this time, if that is even possible in her case.

Porter: "Would you like to book a room, sir?"

Inspector Horace: "I might as well, I am here so much."

Porter: "Are you a regular? I'm just manning the desk."

Inspector Horace: "Indeed, you are. Forget the room. I am Inspector Horace and have an urgent matter to discuss with your manager."

Porter: "It will be about the theft from the safe, I presume."

Inspector Horace: "How do you know about that?"

Porter: "It's all around the hotel. Anyway, there isn't anything a porter doesn't know."

Inspector Horace: "Then, the thief must have covered their tracks by now."

Porter: "If you ask me, it's the waiter who doesn't know his left from his right and repeats everything twice in the same sentence. Obsessed with Charles Dickens, he is writing out copies of the letters that the great man wrote from the hotel, and then delivering to each new guest of the Dickens Suite, as just a means of escaping his duties."

Inspector Horace: "Do you think, on one of those occasions, he might have helped himself to the 'safe' money?"

Porter: "It's as clear as day. Except to the guests who have had rather too much to drink."

Inspector Horace: "But how would he get hold of the key?"

Porter: "Between you and me, the manager has it attached to a chain and inside his pocket. It wouldn't take much for someone to distract him, stick it in a bar of soap when he wasn't looking, and then have an exact copy made."

Inspector Horace: "And what would stop you from doing that?"

Porter: "Nothing, except where would I get the bar of soap from, when they use soap dispensers in the toilets?"

Inspector Horace: "Perhaps I should speak to the manager now?"

[*The porter then rings for the manager who duly arrives.*]

Manager: "Inspector Horace, it is very good to see you, although not under any better circumstances."

Inspector Horace: "To me, they are much better circumstances. My daughter can certainly not be accused of theft this time."

Manager: "Apologies again."

Inspector Horace: "May I ask, was a pair of shoes found by the safe?"

Manager: "Of course not, Inspector Horace."

Inspector Horace: "Then, we are looking for a man. According to your porter, a man with a bar of soap with a friend into forging keys."

Manager: "Don't listen to him. I've only put him on reception because we are short-staffed, and he is always complaining about his back."

[*At that moment, a lady comes running down the stairs in just a bath towel. No more, no less.*]

Towel Lady: "HELP ME! There has been a man inside my en suite. He's also had his hand in my bubbles."

Manager: "Madam, are you sure?"

Towel Lady: "Of course, I'm sure, my soap is missing."

Inspector Horace [*to the manager*]: "Then, this same man must be our thief? Do you have two safes?"

Manager: "No, but the rooms have key cards."

Inspector Horace [*to the lady*]: "Can you describe this man? Presumably, you had both eyes open, unless you were hair washing."

Towel Lady: "I was wearing a mask. I always bathe in a mask."

Inspector Horace: "Then, how did you know it was a man?"

Towel Lady: "It was a man alright."

Manager [*to the lady*]: "I'm sorry for your trauma, expect a reduction in your bill." [*The lady nods her acceptance and returns to her bath.*]

Inspector Horace [*to the porter, with his mobile phone ringing*]: *"*Help me answer it."

[*The porter presses the green button.*]

Porter: "You are okay to speak now."

Inspector Horace [*noticing his daughter's name on the display*]: "What is it Florence?"

Florence: "Don't be mad at me, Father."

Inspector Horace: "What have you been doing now, Florence?"

Florence: "The head teacher says that you will have to collect me. I'm not allowed to be at school without any shoes."

Inspector Horace: "Why are you, Florence?"

Florence: "It's complicated, a boy is involved."

Inspector Horace: "Why don't you just tell your head teacher the truth?"

Florence: "I don't want the boy to think I've grassed on him."

Inspector Horace: "Okay, Florence, if you help me solve my case, I will talk to your head teacher. I am sure I can think of a way around the situation. Everything can be sorted, except perhaps a locked filing cabinet. Is that a deal?"

Florence: "That's a royal flush, Father."

Inspector Horace: "Okay, Florence. Well, you won't believe it, but I'm back at *The Lion Hotel*, investigating another theft."

Florence: "You're not, Father."

Inspector Horace: "I know, I couldn't believe it myself. So, here is the scenario: money has gone missing from the safe, the porter suggests the key must have been copied from the manager's chain, and now a lady has come running saying that a man has stolen her soap."

Florence: "It's quite simple, Father. The porter has stolen the money."

Inspector Horace: "What makes you say that, Florence?"

Florence: "Well, did the lady come running in just a towel?"

Inspector Horace: "Yes, Florence, how did you guess that?"

Florence: "I didn't guess it, Father – it is obvious that the lady and the porter are in on it together. The lady is wearing nothing but her towel for dramatic effect, and it was the porter that suggested the idea of the soap to you in the first place."

Inspector Horace: "Florence, that is brilliant."

Florence: "Don't mention it, Father. Now how are you going to get me out of my soapy mess with the head teacher?"

Inspector Horace: "Put him on the phone, Florence."

Mr Collins: "Is that Florence's father?"

Inspector Horace: "Inspector Horace to whoever is asking."

Mr Collins: "It's Mr Collins, Florence's head teacher. I'm afraid your daughter has rather overstepped the mark this time."

Inspector Horace: "Not him, again."

Mr Collins: "No, not Mark, as in one of our boys, although there is one in your daughter's class. Mark, as in overstepped the mark in relation to an obvious disregard for the school rules."

Inspector Horace: "In what way? When I dropped Florence off at school this morning, she was quite presentable. Her skirt was rolled all the way down, and her tie tied tighter than I felt she would have willingly desired it. Not wearing any shoes, but the rest of her uniform was all there."

Mr Collins: "It was her lack of footwear, or the absence of anything on her feet, that breaks the school uniform policy. The requirement is that all the girls, and obviously boys, too, should have black shoes, no black soles."

Inspector Horace: "I'm afraid it's my fault, I forgot to put my daughter's shoes in the boot of the car, I must have left them on the mat at home with her socks inside. I cannot believe how brave my daughter has been managing without them up until now, not wanting to bother her father whilst he is busy at work."

Mr Collins: "That is indeed admirable, and I must apologise for thinking it a deliberate act on your daughter's part."

Inspector Horace: "An easy mistake to have made."

Florence [*having been handed her mobile phone back by the head teacher*]: "Thank you, Father, for owning up to your mistake. See you this evening with my soles as black as socks."

Inspector Horace: "Florence, take care."

[*Florence cuts her mobile phone off before her father can finish his sentence.*]

Manager [*to Inspector Horace*]: "So, who is our thief?"

Inspector Horace [*looking at the porter*]: "Young man, you are under arrest for the theft of the money from the safe.".

Inspector Horace [*next looking at the manager*]: "I think you need to bring the lady back, too – she is your porter's accomplice."

The manager looks on in amazement at Inspector Horace's way of solving the crime.

The End

Bibliography

Andrew, Lucy, *The Boy Detective in Early British Children's Literature: Patrolling the Borders between Boyhood and Manhood: Critical Approaches to Children's Literature* (London: Palgrave Macmillan, 2017)

Barnes, Justin, *Downton Abbey: Rules for Household Staff* (London: Headline Publishing Group, 2014)

Braben, Eddie, *Eddie Braben's Morecambe & Wise Book* (London: Ebury Press, 2013)

Butterworth, John, *Four Centuries at The Lion Hotel Shrewsbury* (Stone: John Butterworth, 2011)

Carr, Tony, *Shrewsbury: A Pictorial History* (Chichester: Phillimore & Co. Ltd., 1994)

Cromarty, R (ed.), *Shropshire History and Archaeology: Transactions of the Shropshire Archaeological and History Society,* Volume LXXV (Shrewsbury: Shropshire Archaeological and Historical Society, 2000)

Devant, David, *My Magic Life,* Introduction by J. B. Priestley (Bideford: The Supreme Magic Company, 1983)

Dickens, Charles, *The Letters of*, ed. by His Sister-In-Law and his Eldest Daughter (London and New York: Macmillan and Co., 1893)

Eldin, Peter, *Pocket Book of Magic* (London: Kingfisher Books Limited, 1985)

Falk, Peter, *Just One More Thing: Stories from my Life* (London: Arrow, 2008)

Guide to Buildings of Special Architectural or Historical Interest in Shrewsbury, A (Shrewsbury: Shrewsbury and Atcham Borough Council, n.d.)

Hill, Amelia Levitt, *The Complete Book of Table Setting and Flower Arrangement with Service and Etiquette*, 2nd edn (New York: Greystone Press, 1957)

Hinton, Nigel & David Trumper, *Historical Hostelries: A Guide to the Historic Pubs of Shrewsbury between the Bridges* (Shrewsbury: Nigel Hinton, 2005)

Keverne, Richard, *Tales of Old Inns*, 2nd edn (London and Glasgow: Collins, 1947)

Lamb, Geoffrey, *Victorian Magic* (London, Henley & Boston: Routledge & Kegan Paul, 1976)

Lloyd, L. C., *The Inns of Shrewsbury: Their Signs and Their Stories* (Shrewsbury: Shropshire County Library, 1976)

Lynn, Jonathan, *Comedy Rules: From the Cambridge Footlights to Yes Prime Minister* (London: Faber and Faber Limited, 2011)

Patterson, Ian, *Secret Shrewsbury: 900 Years in 90 Minutes or thereabouts* (Bridgnorth: GET Publishing, 2007)

Priestley, J. B., *An Inspector Calls and Other Plays*, Modern Classics (London: Penguin Group, 2000)

Saulles, Mary de, *The Story of Shrewsbury* (Almeley: Logaston Press, 2012)

Appendix

The Lion Hotel Entertainments Bill (1875), *Shropshire Archives* Ref. No. 665/4/483.